Cinders

by Nick Cornall

"With grateful thanks to Jennifer Aston for writing out the music for me."

Edited and Arranged by Alison Hedger

The pantomime story of Cinderella with new songs.

Duration approx. 50 minutes.

For children aged 7 - 11 years.
Key Stage 2

TEACHER'S BOOK
Piano score, complete with the vocal line, song words, chord symbols, recorder melodies and production notes. Opportunities for mime and dance included. Percussion and sound effects may be added as desired.

SONGS

1a. Old London Town	*All**
1b. Just 100 Years Ago	*Solo voice + All*
1c. Get Up, Get Up	*All*
2. No-one Can Resist An Ugly Sister	*Ella, Bella + All*
3. Cinders, Cinders	*Buttons + All**
4. When She Sets Her Eyes On Me	*Prince Charming + All*
5. Then The Moonlight	*Cinders + Buttons*
6. Now I'm Old And Grey	*Fairy Godmother + All*
7. It Fits, It Fits	*Bella + All*
8. When The Old Church Clock	*All**

* indicates recorder parts.

The Pupil's Book, Order No. GA10847, contains the play, song words and appropriate musical parts.

A matching tape cassette of the music for rehearsals and performances is also available, Order No. GA10851, side A with vocals included and side B with vocals omitted .

Order No. GA10833
ISBN 0-7119-3611-0

This page is blank for teacher's own production notes

Nick Cornall has re-told the traditional story of Cinderella in CINDERS. However, there are some novel twists to the characters which make this an easy production to stage. The technical problems of a pumpkin turning into a stagecoach are dispensed with, as the Fairy Godmother is well past her "sell by date", and no longer able to deliver what is expected!

Prince Charming is anything but charming! He is vain and a snob who is keenly searching for a wife — just so long as she is rich and has a double-barrelled name! Definitely not the idyllic match for Cinderella. He gets all he deserves in the ugly sister, Bella.
Buttons follows the traditional character. He obtains a ball ticket for Cinders, but resorts to taking her there himself by piggyback!

The songs are attractive, easy to learn and fun to sing. Alison Hedger has written some recorder parts which are melodies in their own right. Percussion and sound effects can be added throughout as desired.

PRODUCTION NOTES

Characters	Speaking parts	Solo singing
Children		
Mice		
Cinderella	/	/
Buttons	/	/
Ella ⎫ The Ugly Sisters	/	/
Bella ⎭		
Prince Charming	/	/
King	/	
Fairy Godmother	/	/
Sir William Carter	/	
Heralds 1	/	
2	/	
3	/	
Footman	/	
Footman 1	/	
2	/	
Servant	/	
Prince's friend		
Ball Guests		

Ample opportunities arise for dance sequences, especially for the mice and ball guests.

There are 6 scenes and only two sets: the kitchen and the palace.
The story takes place in old London town approximately 100 years ago.
The opening representation of a London square has no need of a backdrop.

CINDERS was written for performing in the round, but it will be very successful when performed on a traditional stage, and will involve just two sets of scenery.

The principal props include a broom, bench, magic wand, pogo stick and a golden shoe.

The lighting and costumes are as available.

Nick Cornall wrote CINDERS for mixed 7–11 year olds, encompassing the wide range of ability normally found in a Primary school. The major parts hopefully stretch the more able, while the smaller parts allow children of any ability to take part. The cast can be extended to include more mice, children, ball guests, royal attendants etc. CINDERS works equally well with small groups or single classes, in which case some doubling of on-stage non-speaking parts can be a help.

The musicians and singers have an important role to play in the production, and they can be dressed in costume if they too wish to enjoy the fun of dressing up.

A tape of the songs is available and will be a great help with learning the music and rehearsals. The B-side of the tape has no vocal tracks and is for use in performances. (*Catalogue number GA 10851*)

"May I recommend involving parents in your production of CINDERS as a supportive choir? They are a real help when nervous voices become dry under stage lights. Two rehearsals are usually sufficient. The sense of enjoyment, participation, sharing and contribution will long be remembered by the whole school community. Enjoy CINDERS!"

Nick Cornall

Song 1a, 1b and 1c are unbroken.
Mime during the songs reflects the lyrics. (See the Pupil's play booklet.)

Song 1a

OLD LONDON TOWN

All + Recorders and Chimes.

Cinders is seen sweeping during the song.

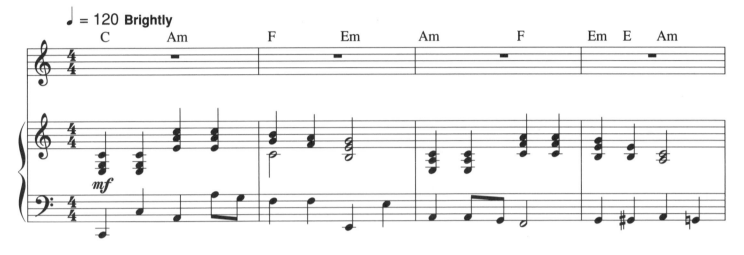

5

JUST 100 YEARS AGO

Solo voice + All.

Cinders is seen feeding the mice during the song.

With feeling - slightly slower

1. Just one hun - dred years a - go, by St. Clem - ent's bells, sat a girl with tear - ful eyes, in old Lon - don

Straight into song 1c

9

Song 1c

GET UP, GET UP

All.

The two ugly sisters enter during song, and exit at the end.

By close of the song Cinders has retired to her sleeping place in the kitchen.

Wash those pans,_____ dirt-y your hands. Sweep the cob-webs from the door._____
Plates and cups need wash - ing up. Let us see the sil - ver shine._____

On your knees, use el - bow grease, po - lish up the floor. 2.Get
Beat these rugs and clean those jugs. Don't go wast - ing time. 3.Get

up, get up, you sleep - y head, there's work_____ to do a - round

here.   COME ON CINDERS,

YOU LAZY GIRL!

Get up, get up, you sleep - y head, there's work to do a - round here. Lots of love - ly work to do.

Song 2

NO ONE CAN RESIST AN UGLY SISTER

Ella, Bella + All.

Cue: With true beauty, quite so rare?

Prin - cess. The oth - er's loss will be the Prin - ce's gain!

Last time only

Fine

Last time only

Fine

4. We have got the kind of looks that drive the fel - las mad, 'spec - ially when we're all dressed up we're

real - ly not that bad! And so,

Return to beginning of song for All to repeat verses 1, 2 and 3 with altered words, as indicated.

15

CINDERS, CINDERS

Buttons, All, Recorders + Optional Triangle.

Dance for Cinderella and mice during instrumental section.

Cue: With your own exclusive mop.

Recorders - Instrumental section for dance (plays with repeat of music for verses 1, 2, 3 and 5)

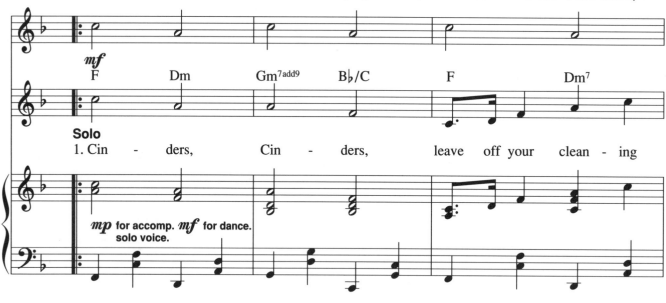

Solo

1. Cin - ders, Cin - ders, leave off your clean - ing

wind - ers! You are the light of my life.

Please stop your scrub - bing, dust - ing and rub - bing. Soon we'll be run - ning a -

way. 2. It's hard to see you be - ing so

sad and so low. Why don't you give the

19

thing I could to take you off with me.

D⁷   Gm⁷   C⁷

Recorders

All: 5. Cin - de - rel - la, he'll be your fav' - rite

F   Dm   Gm⁷ᵃᵈᵈ⁹   B♭ᵐᵃʲ⁷/C   F   Dm⁷

fel - la.   You are his heart's des - ire____ Please stop your cry - ing,

Gm⁷ᵃᵈᵈ⁴   B♭ᵐᵃʲ⁷/C   Am⁷   A⁷   Dm⁷   F   B♭

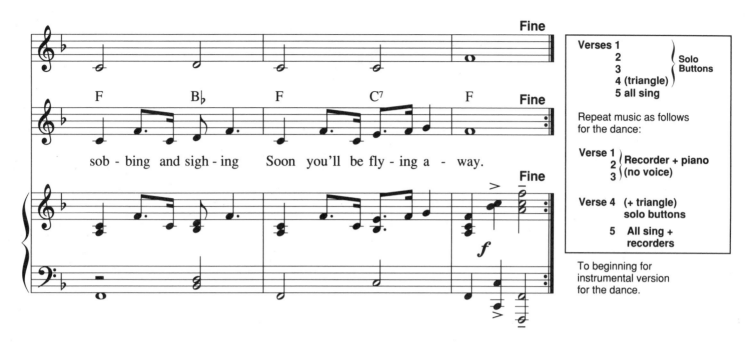

Verses 1
2 } Solo Buttons
3
4 (triangle)
5 all sing

Repeat music as follows for the dance:

Verse 1
2 } Recorder + piano (no voice)
3

Verse 4 (+ triangle) solo buttons
5 All sing + recorders

To beginning for instrumental version for the dance.

sob - bing and sigh - ing Soon you'll be fly - ing a - way.

MUSIC TO CLOSE SCENE ONE

Cue: What would I do without him?

Song 4

WHEN SHE SETS HER EYES ON ME

Prince Charming + All.

Cue: And a bank account to match.

MUSIC TO CLOSE SCENE TWO

Cue: For names, his score is nought!

THEN THE MOONLIGHT

Cinders + Buttons

Cue: And me without a frock! Women!

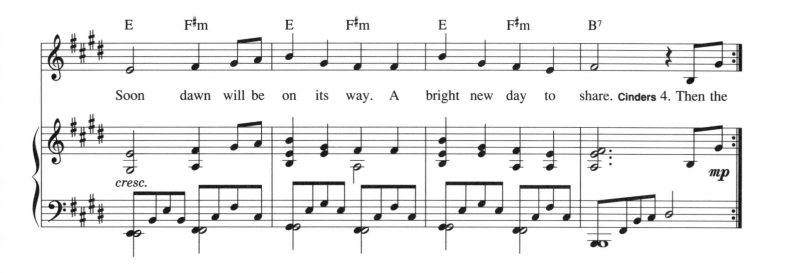

Soon dawn will be on its way. A bright new day to share. **Cinders** 4. Then the

MUSIC TO CLOSE SCENE THREE

Straight in after close of previous song ♩ = 100

NOW I'M OLD AND GREY

Fairy Godmother + All.

Cue: Although I'm not sure how.

all.   I'm a to - tal fail - ure and I've had my
all.   She's a to - tal fail - ure and she's had her

day.   Now I'm get - ting old and grey.
day.   Now she's get - ting old and

now she's get - ting old and, now she's get - ting old and grey.

30

OPENING MUSIC TO SCENE FIVE

Guests arriving at the ball.

✳ See note at foot of page

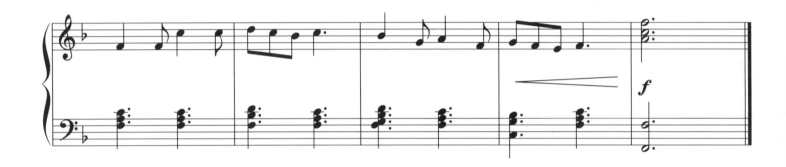

MUSIC TO CLOSE SCENE FIVE

Cue: And go home in her vest!

♩. = 100

mf

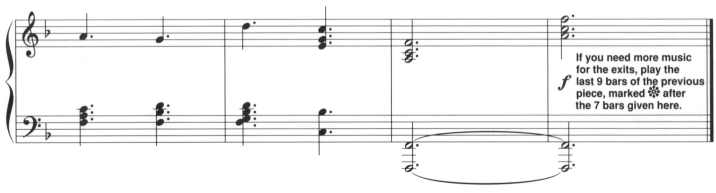

If you need more music
for the exits, play the
last 9 bars of the previous
piece, marked ✳ after
the 7 bars given here.

32

IT FITS, IT FITS

All + Bella.

Cue: A perfect fit! A perfect fit!

Positively ♩. = 100

fits, it fits, it real - ly fits, there is - n't an - y doubt of it. The prince is feel - ing

quite a twit! It fits, it fits, it fits.

35

Song 8

WHEN THE OLD CHURCH CLOCK

All + Recorders.

Add twelve church chimes as desired.

Cue: Happily ever after.

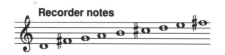

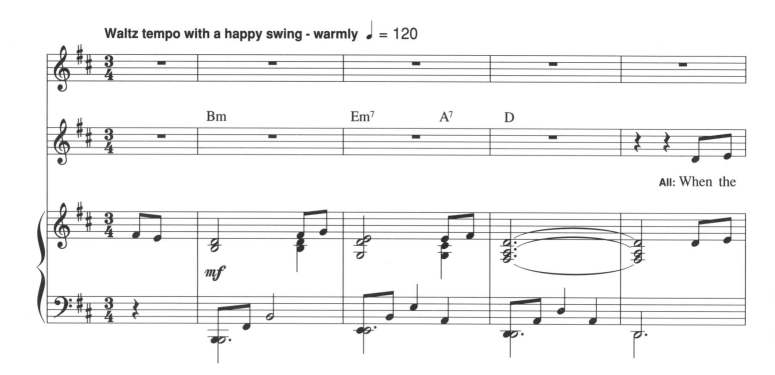

36

Bm   D   Em⁷   A   D

stars ap - pear o - ver - head.   When the Lon - don

G   D   Bm   Em⁷   A⁷

square is bathed in moon - light, that's the time Cin - de - rel - la goes to

D   A⁷   D   Dᵈⁱᵐ

bed.   All her dreams make her heart dance with

glee. A new life full of sun-shine she sees.

When the old church clock is chim - ing mid -

night. That's the time Cin-de-rel - la goes to bed

When the rel - la goes to bed.

For exits and taking of bows, play music from Song 1a OLD LONDON TOWN, pages 5,6 and 7.

Printed in the United Kingdom by Caligraving Limited, Thetford, Norfolk.

8/94(18576)